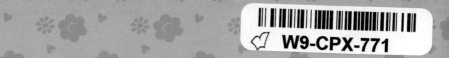

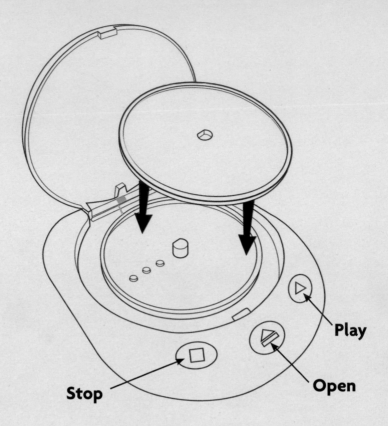

Play

Stop

Open

How to Use the Music Player
Use your music discs to create the perfect atmosphere for the stories as you read.

- Each disc has a picture of a character on it. Find the disc that matches the story you are reading.

- Open the music player by pressing the middle button ⏏. Insert the disc and close the lid. When you are ready to play a tune as indicated in the story, press the button on the right ▷. To play the next tune, press the right-hand button again ▷. To stop the music at any time during play, press the left-hand button ☐.

- When the player is stopped in the middle of a tune, it will then resume that tune when the play button is pressed again.

- After a period of non-use, the player will shut off. When the play button is pressed again, the player will go back to the first tune on the disc.

Happy Bow Day!

written by Elizabeth Bennett

studio fun BOOKS

White Plains, New York • Montréal, Québec • Bath, United Kingdom

SONG 1

Hello, everyone!
Welcome to my bow-tique!

I'd love for you to meet my animal friends.
This adorable puppy is Shelby. Figaro is my
dear, sweet cat. Cuckoo Loca is the pretty
little bird, and Lollipop is the hamster.
I love making bows for all of them.

Shelby can't wait for me to make a bow for her. Hold on, Shelby! I'll be ready as soon as I say good-bye to Daisy!

I made Shelby two bows that are shaped like dog bones. Shelby loves them. Doesn't she look wonderful?

Oh, no! Figaro got into trouble while I was busy. What a mess! His yellow bow is ruined.

Don't worry, Figaro. I love you no matter what! Let's find a new bow for you.

Here you go, Figaro. This bow with the little fish on it is perfect!

SONG 4

Oh, here comes Cuckoo Loca. She loves to wear pretty bows on her head. Doesn't she look sweet in this pink one?

Now it's Lollipop's turn. But where did that little hamster go? Lollipop! Where are you?

There you are, Lollipop. I think I'll make you a bow with bells on it. Then I'll always be able to find you. *Ring-a-ling*!

I just love making bows. And I especially love making bows for my friends! A bow day is always a happy day!

BATTERY INFORMATION

To remove or insert replaceable batteries, remove safety screw from battery compartment door. Lift and remove door. Take out and safely dispose of old batteries. Follow polarity diagram inside compartment to insert two new batteries of any of the following types: AA or LR6 or equivalent. Alkaline batteries are recommended. Put battery compartment door back and secure safety screw. Do not use excess force or an improper type or size screwdriver.

CAUTION

To ensure proper safety and operation, battery replacement must always be done by an adult. Never let a child use this product unless battery door is secure. Keep batteries away from small children and immediately dispose of any used batteries safely.

GENERAL SAFETY AND CARE

• Rechargeable batteries are not to be used in this product.
• Non-rechargeable batteries are not to be recharged.
• Different types of batteries or new and used batteries are not to be mixed.
• Batteries are to be inserted with the correct polarity.
• Exhausted batteries are to be removed from the toy.
• The supply terminals are not to be short-circuited.
• Do not mix old and new batteries.
• Do not mix alkaline, standard (carbon-zinc) or rechargeable (nickel-cadmium) batteries.
• Prevent the book and unit from getting wet and avoid exposure to excessively hot or cold temperatures.
• Remove batteries when not in use or discharged.